Workbook

Fast Like a Girl

An Essential Guide

To

Dr. Mindy Pelz's Book

Genie Reads

Table of Contents

How To Use This Workbook

Hello there!

It is with great pleasure to see that you have taken an interest in the book "*Fast Like a Girl*" by Dr. Mindy Pelz. If you have been trying out different diets and fasts but none seem to be working out on a longer-term basis, do not despair. You have come to the right place! As the title says, when you learn to fast like a girl, it delivers healthy weight loss, energy and vitality boosts as well as the various excellent healing effects that you have heard so much about from folks who fast regularly.

This workbook is meant to enhance and highlight the ideas and concepts mentioned, so that it makes it very much easier for you to take action and implement what you have learnt from the book into practical, daily usage. With the aid of this workbook, activating and maintaining your body's natural healing mechanisms becomes much easier through the step-by-step guidance and systematic approaches highlighted within. Equipped with the knowledge and practical skillsets developed through the workbook's exercises, you will be able to integrate fasting into your daily routine in a proper, sustained fashion while enjoying the various health benefits conferred by an optimally executed fast. In order to absorb quicker and with a lasting impact, it is vital that you answer all the questions presented in the workbook, and answer them sincerely. Only by digging deep and giving honest answers will you be able to flash light on what truly matters to you, and get the opportunities to effect lasting positive change in your daily life.

The workbook will also feature important summaries of each individual chapter, which will be integral in helping you answer the questions contained therein. As such, for the time constrained folk, you do not necessarily need to read the main book before answering the questions in this workbook. All the crucial points have been condensed and captured for your attention. For the folks whom have already read the book, the afore mentioned salient concepts will serve well as quick reminders and gentle nudges when you are doing the questions.

Whilst attempting the questions found in the workbook, please take your time to go through it carefully. This portion is an area where speedy reading can be set aside and replaced with thoughtful ruminations. The questions will encourage you to reflect and think, sometimes very deeply, before you jump in with any answers. It will be of great benefit to you if the answers supplied are colored with the honesty of thought and tinged with sincerity. After all, no one can be as interested in your welfare as your own self.

Done in this careful, constructive way, you will be able to harness the positive change created and see it reverberate throughout many aspects of your life. For some, the honest answers may create self criticism. Take heart, know that you are not alone, and that by just the mere act of acknowledgement of mistakes made in the past, that itself is a very important step forward.

You will want to come back to these questions again after your initial foray, say after a period of 4 to 8 weeks; there really is no set in stone time length, but it is highly recommended to have at least a space of 4 weeks between the first and second attempt at the questions. This second try is really to let you see the progress you have made, both in thoughts and actions, and also to think of different angles to the same questions with your new life experiences.

You can really repeat this process as many times as you find useful. The key is always honesty in the answers and an indefatigable spirit for self development and progress.

May you be well and be happy.

Introduction

With her book "Fast Like a Girl", Dr. Mindy Pelz introduces a new paradigm about healthcare, highlighting the concerning rise of long-term conditions that have an impact on women. In her search for answers, she found herself sitting in the office of one of the top medical doctors in the world who diagnosed her with chronic fatigue syndrome, a condition for which there was no known cure. He told her it would take years for her to heal from such a debilitating condition and then instructed her to drop out of school, hop onto trial medications, and hope that her body would heal.

That dark moment taught Dr. Pelz one important lesson that she has carried forward into her practice today: When your health falls apart, you need just one person to believe in you and give you hope. She pressed on from that dark moment and heeded the advice of another doctor who suggested a more natural way of healing: simple change of the eating habits as well as the foods consumed. She was in awe of how quickly her body responded to the new diet changes. Yet it also left her wondering how many people are given similar grim prognosis who never get taught the effect food has on our body's ability to heal.

What has changed in the past 30 years that has us on a collision course with chronic disease? When one looks at the root causes of many chronic diseases, there is a common thread — poor metabolic health.

The term metabolic health is often used to refer to a person's ability to properly regulate their blood sugar, blood pressure, and cholesterol without the use of medications. Not only does poor metabolic health led to chronic disease, but it also compromises the immune system. Perhaps the most startling part of having poor metabolic health is that as a culture we have normalized this condition. Many of the hallmark signs that indicate a person's metabolic health is diminishing are often given a label by doctors as "aging," "genetic," or "unavoidable.

A classic sign of a failing metabolism that is rarely addressed is a person's inability to go without food.

In Fast Like a Girl, Dr. Mindy teaches you how to use fasting as the shortest route to greater health so that you may regain control of your health.

Dr. Mindy will instruct you on:

- how to transition from eating all day to intermittent fasting (13-15 hours)
- how to safely fast longer if you wish (15 72 hours)
- how to pace your fasting according to your menstrual cycle
- the greatest meals to eat after a fast to improve metabolic health

Now, take a deep breath and close your eyes. Try to picture an alternate reality that looks different – but better – than where you are currently. If you can successfully create a wonderful image of what you're aiming for, then you're ready for anything. But if you see nothing just yet, don't get discouraged. This workbook will help you. Let's Get To It

PART 1: The Science

Ch 1: It's Not Your Fault

Summary

Just imagine your body as the coolest machine ever invented! It's made up of more than 30 trillion cells that act like a unified team, all cooperating and working hard in making sure you stay healthy. Each individual cell functions like a small factory that produces energy by burning fat, breaking down nutrients and manufacturing antioxidants. These cells know when to power you up with energy so you can perform a task, and when to slow you down so that you can rest. It's truly remarkable!

But here's the challenge: they need your support. In order to function properly, your body needs certain nutrients such as beneficial fats, amino acids that make proteins, as well as important vitamins and minerals. When they lack that support, they face challenges in performing their job. That's why trendy diets have let you down before. Most quick-fix diets work against your body's design, making it impossible to get a long-term result, instead they set you up for numerous health problems that accelerate aging and put you on a path to chronic disease.

Let's discuss five ways in which diets have led you down a twisty path. These are called "the failed five":

First up is calorie restriction. We've often heard that eating fewer calories is the key to losing weight. We call this approach to dieting the "calorie in, calorie out" theory, and it's one of the hardest ways to lose weight permanently. Every time you eat less and exercise more, you change your metabolic set point. When you go back to eating more calories or working out less, the pounds come back on much easier because you are above your set point threshold. Because of the change it makes to your set point, it's incredibly hard to succeed at low-calorie diets long term. Although it dates back to the 1960s, the Minnesota Starvation experiment is still revered as the most prominent study ever done on the physical, emotional, and social changes that happen when the human body is put into a calorie-restricted state for long periods. When administering this low-calorie diet, researchers noticed several dramatic negative changes to the physical and mental health of their subjects.

The 2nd challenge is making poor food-quality choices. When the food industry replaced fat with sugar and flavor enhancing chemicals in its products, this caused obesity rates to skyrocket. Equate low fat to high-sugar, highly toxic ingredients—two things that will quickly cause you to pack on the pounds. Why did these new trendy low-fat food products cause us to gain weight? Mainly due to insulin resistance. Insulin resistance is a condition in which your cells can no longer successfully use insulin as a hormone to escort the sugar from your food into your cells. Insulin is your sugar-storing hormone. Your pancreas releases this hormone after you eat a meal to escort the sugar from that meal into your cells. A constant influx of insulin will flood your cells, overwhelming the receptor sites that allow the hormone to perform its job.

Next, let's talk about cortisol surges. Cortisol which is a stress hormone is the enemy of insulin. The rigidity of these diets often creates stress, spiking your cortisol levels. This new agitated state creates a fight-or-flight reaction in your brain, and your brain responds by releasing cortisol into your bloodstream, telling your body there is a crisis at hand. Your body responds to this crisis signal by shutting down digestion, halting fat burning, and raising your glucose levels so that you are physically prepared to handle this stressful situation. As your glucose levels go up, insulin rises to meet the new sugar demands. Often cortisol spikes can happen when you hop on a diet that is restrictive and hard to fit into your lifestyle. Cortisol can also rise when you are over exercising, trying to force your body into a state of health. You can`t be in constant states of stress and improve your health at the same time. You may have noticed this when implementing a new diet while living your rushing woman's lifestyle.

The 4th challenge is exposure to toxic ingredients. When your body gets an influx of these chemicals it doesn't know how to break them down, so it stores them as fat. Your body literally didn't know how to break down the chemicals in your food, so it placed them in your fat stores such that it wouldn't harm the organs that keep you alive. Much like a flood of insulin blocks receptor sites on the outside of your cells, so do obesogens. Detoxing these chemicals out of your body can be the answer to a variety of health challenges, including weight-loss resistance, thyroid problems, and autoimmune conditions. When you stop to read the ingredients of many prepackaged diet foods, you'll see that they are laden with chemicals.

Lastly, we face the challenge of depending on one-size-fits-all approaches. We all have different hormonal needs at different times of our lives, and our diet needs to accommodate that ebb and flow. If you are a properly menstrual cycling woman, most diets have you eating the same way all month long, possibly working against the needs of your hormones. The exciting part of accepting this is you will see that as a woman there is a better way to approach our relationship with food, one that is built on adapting our diet to our menstrual cycles. The massive number of hormonal issues women face today—like infertility, breast cancer, and polycystic ovary syndrome— can often be alleviated by learning to tune our lifestyle needs to our monthly cycle. Instead of trying to create our own beautiful unique health path, we watch other women and the results they get with their diets and assume our body can achieve the same result. As you learn to fast like a girl, keep in mind that even though we are all living in a female body, we don't all have the same lifestyle needs. Finding a diet that is customized to our hormones is pivotal if we want to succeed at our health.

Take some time to accept yourself. No doubt you've seen some successes of friends who went on fad diets, and you try to replicate their accomplishments, only to realize you can't achieve the same results and the anxiety as well as stress from this starts to add up. It can also be frustrating when you go to your doctor for answers on a health issue only to be berated and told you need to lose weight and just imbibe the one-size-fits-all pharmaceutical solutions that has often been shown to be ineffective. After spending countless hours at the gym, trying to improve your fitness, you might be questioning if there is something genetically wrong with you. Just drop these beliefs. As you enter a new path to better health, they will not benefit you in the least.

The figures speak loudly about the health issues that women face today. Obesity, high blood pressure, cancer, diabetes, and other diseases affect a sizable section of the population. It's time to reclaim your vigor and work for better health. Healing begins with self-forgiveness and the realization that the shortcomings of traditional diets are not a reflection of your worth or abilities.

Change your perspective and embrace a new health paradigm. You have the power to write your own health story. By understanding the failed five and recognizing the limitations of traditional diets, you may break free from the restraints of diet culture and embark on a journey towards enhanced health and well-being.

There is a girl named Sarah, who is a subscriber of Dr. Mindy Pelz's YouTube channel. She lost weight and improved her health by embracing fasting principles. Doctors had previously informed her that she was on a fast track to developing diabetes and that she should lose weight by cutting calories and choosing low-fat, sugar-free foods. Frustrated with empty answers from her doctor about her poor metabolic health, Sarah turned to YouTube to solve her own health challenges. She sent her doctor to Dr. Pelz's channel, where he dove into the research and started encouraging his female patients to fast, recommending Dr. Pelz's videos as a resource to learn how to fast properly.

Get ready to fast like a girl and discover the incredible possibilities that lie ahead!

Lessons

1. Take care of yourself personally: Understand that your body is unique and needs individualized attention when it comes to diet and health. Find a personalized approach that suits your specific needs for long-term wellness.

2. Choose quality over quantity: Instead of focusing on quantity, prioritize the quality of the food you eat. Opt for nutrient-rich whole foods rather than processed options. The quality of your diet directly affects your

hormones balance, weight management, and overall health.

3. Manage stress effectively: Stress management is vital for your well-being. Chronic stress disrupts your hormonal balance and hampers progress towards your health goals. Incorporate relaxation techniques, self-care practices, and healthy coping strategies to effectively manage stress and maintain optimal health

Issues Surrounding the Subject Matter

1. Have you ever felt let down by diets that promised quick results but didn't deliver lasting success? How did it make you feel and how did you cope with it?

2. Are you aware of the impact of food quality on your overall well-being? Do you prioritize consuming nutritious, whole foods to support your body's functions?

3. How do you manage stress in your daily life? Are there any strategies or practices you find effective in reducing stress and maintaining a healthy balance?

Goals

1. Achieve sustainable and long-term weight loss by adopting a holistic approach that supports the body's natural functions and metabolism.

2. Improve overall health and well-being by making informed food choices and prioritizing nutrient-dense, whole foods that nourish the body.

3. Cultivate a healthy relationship with food and body, letting go of guilt and embracing self-acceptance, while focusing on individual needs and unique hormonal balance.

Action Steps

1. Learn about nutrition and its impact on your body.
   a. Spend 10 minutes each day reading nutrition articles or watching educational videos.
   b. Follow credible nutrition experts on digital platforms for helpful tips and insights.

2. Adopt a balanced and personalized approach to eating.
   a. Fill your plate with a variety of plant-based foods during every meal.
   b. Practice mindful eating by listening to your body's hunger and fullness cues.

3. Prioritize self-care and stress management.
    a. Take a five-minute walk outside to clear your mind and reduce stress.
    b. Dedicate 10 minutes each day to a relaxation practice, such as deep breathing for meditation.

Checklist

1. Make sure you are giving your body the nutrients it needs to eat healthy fats, proteins, vitamins and minerals.

2. Stay away from popular diets that conflict with your body's function and can cause health problems later.

3. Choose whole, natural foods over processed foods and limit sugary and artificial foods to stay healthy.

Ch 2: The Healing Power of Fasting

Summary

Cycling between times of famine and feasting was the way of life for prehistoric ancestors. Because of this, many scientists believe that these harsh evolutionary conditions created a new genotype within humans—a genotype that gives their bodies the necessary cellular tools to adapt to the cycles of fasting and feasting.

The current approach of eating all day without ever dipping into periods of fasting goes against their genetic code.

A look back in history reveals several examples of how the human body thrives in a fasted state. Although done for spiritual reasons, Ramadan fasting is one of the greatest examples of how the human body positively adapts to long windows of time without food.

Hippocrates, the father of modern medicine, used fasting as one of his primary healing tools.

Hippocrates used healing therapies that were built around strengthening the body's own innate resistance to disease, and one of those therapies looked much like intermittent fasting and the ketogenic diet.

In this complex modern world, where food is available 24/7, is fasting the key healing tool we've forgotten? This chapter explains what a fasted state looks like in this modern day, the healing mechanisms that are getting turned on while in this state, and how the science is revealing that longer fasts can turn on more healing switches within the cells that may confer a multitude of benefits, particularly for women.

The best place to start is to understand what it means to fast and that the human body has two fuel systems which the cells get their energy from, so the body can function: sugar and fat.

The first system, called the sugar burner energy system, gets activated while eating. Eating food raises blood sugar. Our cells sense this influx of sugar in the blood and use that sugar, called glucose, as fuel for the thousands of functions they perform.

The gradual decline of glucose in the blood as it is used up triggers the cells to switch over to the second energy system, called the ketogenic energy system, or the fat burner system. Although everyone will make this switch differently, research shows that it takes about eight hours after the last meal for the body to shift to its fat-burning system.

If someone has never gone longer than eight hours without food, there is a likelihood that they may have never experienced the healing benefits of the fat-burning energy system.

Dr Pelz reviewed more than 85 studies and declared that intermittent fasting should be used as the first line of treatment for obesity, diabetes, cardiovascular disease, neurodegenerative brain conditions, and cancer. This meta-analysis highlighted several key cellular healing responses that happen when someone periodically flips the metabolic switch and moves into the fat-burning system.

These healing benefits include increased ketones, increased mitochondrial stress resistance, increased antioxidant defenses, increased autophagy, increased DNA repair, decreased glycogen, decreased insulin, decreased mTOR (The name mTOR comes from "mechanistic target of rapamycin". It is a protein that acts as a key regulator of cell growth and metabolism in the body), and decreased protein synthesis.

Numerous studies are also proving that, outside of the above cellular changes, the most important part of improving metabolic health is changing when to eat, not what to eat.

The first such study in The Journal of Nutrition, Health, and Aging in 2018 showed that obese individuals saw dramatic metabolic improvement despite eating whatever they wanted as long as they ate that food within an 8-hour eating window, leaving 16 hours for fasting.

Both studies show very clearly that when you condense the eating window, leaving more time for fasting, it will help you reduce total body fat percentage, reduce visceral fat, reduce waist circumference, lower blood pressure, decrease LDL cholesterol and decrease hemoglobin A1c (Hemoglobin A1c is a form of hemoglobin that has glucose attached to it, and measuring its levels in the blood provides an estimate of a person's average blood sugar control over the previous 2-3 months).

In a modern world where humans have been conditioned to eat low-quality food all day long, research like this gives hope that metabolic damage that is causing so many to struggle with poor health can be reversed. Changing the time period to eat is more important than the actual quality of the food individuals eat. This is great news if humans are to improve metabolic health.

These studies prove the benefits that allowed prehistoric ancestors to thrive when food was absent. Not only are individuals burning energy from fat, but also accelerating weight loss and lowering blood pressure and cholesterol.

Lessons

1. Humans have a genetic tendency to cycle between fasting and feasting, a habit that runs back to our prehistoric ancestors.

2. Fasting has been used as medicine throughout history, with prominent individuals like Hippocrates using it into their medical practice.

3. Scientific research has shown that fasting triggers different kinds of cellular healing responses, leading to metabolic benefits such as increased ketones, DNA repair and overall metabolic health.

Issues Surrounding the Subject Matter

1. Considering how our prehistoric ancestors fasted and feasted cycles created genetic differences between us, what have you thought about their impact on modern health?

2. What are your thoughts about using fasting as a healing tool following in the healing modalities of historical figures like Hippocrates.

3. Since now you know that cellular benefits can be drawn from fasting including improved metabolic health shifts to increased ketones and most importantly for this discussion, improved chance of survival. Considering these facts, how might that influence your approach to health and wellness?

Goals

1. Understand the historical significance of fasting and feast cycles in mankind's life.

2. Study the mechanisms and benefits associated with fasts as a healing strategy.

3. Apply intermittent fasts to improve metabolic health, treat specific diseases.

Action Steps

1. Gain knowledge about fasting:
    a. Read books, articles and watch documentaries on fasting.
    b. Join online communities or forums to gain insights from inquisitive fast experiences.

2. Explore healing mechanisms involving fasting's effects:
    a. Follow experts and trusted resources detailing fast impacts on human body systems.

3. Implement intermittent fasting:
    a. Begin with a beginner-friendly fasting approach, like the 16:8 method.
    b. Keep track of your fasting progress and health changes using journals or apps.

Checklist

1. Learn about fasting and its historical relevance.

2. Understand the healing mechanisms and cellular benefits of fasting.

3. Consider intermittent fasting as a strategy that might be used to improve metabolic health, or certain health conditions.

Ch 3: Metabolic Switching: The Missing Key to Weight Loss

Summary

The human body has an astounding capacity to continuously regenerate itself. Old cells are constantly dying off and being replaced by new cells. Different parts of the body regenerate at varying speeds - skin cells turnover approximately every 2-4 weeks, stomach lining cells renew roughly every 5 days, and liver cells replace themselves somewhere between 150-500 days.

Unfortunately, when cells become diseased or damaged, they tend to replicate more dysfunctional cells of the same kind. Once a cell becomes dysfunctional, it often loses the ability to produce healthy new cells. This means that if one wants to truly harness the body's inherent regenerative potential for healing, it is imperative to find ways of renewing healthy cell lines instead of merely replicating more sick ones.

One of the most powerful ways to do this is through an ancient biohacking technique called metabolic switching. Metabolic switching refers to alternating between burning glucose and ketones for fuel. It activates cleansing mechanisms during the fasted state while still allowing growth processes during the fed state. This stimulates autophagy, mTOR pathways, hormetic stressors, and repairs mitochondria and neurons - all critical components of cellular regeneration.

Autophagy can be thought of as a cellular cleansing program. It identifies dysfunctional, old or diseased components in the cell and marks them for recycling. One of the most reliable ways to trigger high levels of autophagy is through fasting for longer than 17 hours. This gives cells the chance to take out the trash and conduct some self-maintenance.

On the flip side, the mTOR pathway stimulates growth of new tissues and cells when nutrients are abundant. This is characteristic of the fed state, when glucose is available from a recent meal. mTOR can help regenerate muscle cells, support hormone production, and even regrow insulin-producing pancreatic beta cells.

Both autophagy and mTOR are essential pathways - the body needs time in each state. Too much autophagy without any mTOR activity will lead to excessive breakdown of tissues such as muscle. Too much mTOR without giving time for autophagy will rapidly accelerate aging. The key is finding the proper balance between cleansing autophagy and building mTOR to gain regeneration benefits from both cleaning house and growing new tissues.

Intermittent fasting also activates an important biological process called hormesis. Hormesis refers to low-level stressors that provoke adaptation and improved functioning in response. It's similar to how exercising stresses the muscles so they'll grow stronger. Fasting creates mild biological stress that prompts our cells to build up their defenses and become more resilient. To maintain this beneficial adaptive response, it's important to vary the duration and challenge of fasting periods periodically. We need just the right amount of hormetic stress from fasting to trigger genes and pathways for adaptation and self-renewal without overdoing it. Fasting provides the perfect hormetic impetus for our cells to grow stronger. By periodically challenging our biology through fasting while allowing recovery time, we can harness the power of hormesis to boost overall functioning and health.

In addition to facilitating cellular recycling and growth, fasting may also directly slow aging by increasing expression of genes like SIRT1. These genes boost cellular defenses and protect against early mortality. Even just 3 weeks of intermittent fasting has been shown to significantly upregulate SIRT1 activity.

Fasting can also unlock metabolic flexibility to burn through stored glucose, making it excellent for sustainable weight loss. Many with obesity have impaired metabolic switching between burning glucose and ketones. Reestablishing this flexibility enables their bodies to begin releasing unnecessary glucose reserves from the liver.

The brain stands to benefit tremendously from intermittent fasting as well. Neurons require both glucose and ketones for optimal functioning. An extended fast supplies the brain with ample ketones to repair damage and forge new neural connections. Refeeding the body provides necessary nutrients to support neuron health. This coupling of fasting and feeding may enhance most aspects of cognition.

The versatile gut microbiome also responds well to periodic fasting. During the fasted state, cleansing processes in the gut improve the local environment. Upon refeeding with prebiotics and probiotics, populations of beneficial bacteria flourish. Together this boosts microbial diversity and healthy intestinal function.

Of all applications, preventing cancer may be one of the most valuable uses of biohacked fasting. Since cancer often originates from dysfunctional mitochondria, intermittent fasting's ability to repair and upgrade mitochondria could prevent or stall the progression of cancer. Those at high risk of cancer may want to consider adopting a daily 14 hour fast.

The cumulative effects of intermittent fasting carry benefits throughout the entire body - liver, muscles, skin, and other tissues. It provides metabolic flexibility to burn excess fuel during fasts and growth factors to regenerate afterward. No pharmaceutical product can match the regenerative potential of this natural biohack.

By aligning lifestyle with our primal cycles of feast and famine, the body taps into its intrinsic healing intelligence. This capacity has become obscured and disabled by the constant convenience store foods of modern life. Biohacking fasting helps strip away these limitations, allowing chronic diseases to be healed, aging to be slowed or reversed, and innate vitality to shine through.

Looking at the mechanisms of metabolic switching through an ancestral lens provides insight into how our bodies evolved to move between periods of fasting and feeding. Our early hunter-gatherer ancestors did not have constant access to food. After burning through their sugar reserves, they would tap into fat-burning ketosis while searching for their next meal. This fasting state allowed for cellular repair processes before they shifted back into the fed state upon eating, spurring growth. These natural cycles of fasting and feeding provided balance.

Today's modern lifestyle of constant eating from dawn to dusk disrupts this ancestral rhythm. We remain stuck perpetually burning sugar and accumulating cellular damage. The result is chronic disease, accelerated aging, and loss of vitality. When we fast intermittently, we realign with our intrinsic need for balance between breakdown and growth.

Beyond cleansing and growth, perhaps the most profound benefit metabolic switching confers is optimization of mitochondria - the powerhouses of our cells. Mitochondria generate energy and glutathione to detoxify. Fasting generates ketones to fuel mitochondria and enhance their function. Refeeding provides key nutrients to support them. Upgraded mitochondria translates to upgraded health and longevity.

While the mechanisms and benefits of fasting have become well elucidated by science, anecdotal experience demonstrates equally powerful effects. One physician, Dr. Terry Wahls, cured her progressive multiple sclerosis with a nutritional ketosis protocol after initially declining despite having the best drugs. Another, Dr. David Perlmutter, has witnessed fasting produce remarkable benefits for all types of brain disorders in his neurology clinic. And Dr. Joseph Mercola, leading natural medicine physician, fasts for over 18 hours daily in his 70s with the energy of a young man. Their clinical results mirror the science.

Such healing potential remain untapped for the majority still unaware of fasting's immense therapeutic value. Yet a grassroots movement has been growing, shared through books, blogs and videos, as people discover fasting's benefits for themselves. Millions of individuals now intermittently fast to biohack their health. But the work has only just begun. We have yet to reach the tipping point required for societal transformation back to our natural evolutionary cycles of feast and famine. But the systems in place will ultimately bend to the wisdom of biology. The black holes of disease sucking our vitality will be gradually displaced by radiant health and longevity through the power of metabolic regeneration.

Lessons

1. Humans evolved with natural cycles of fasting and feeding. Intermittent fasting helps restore this balance for modern people.

2. Metabolic switching confers many benefits like slowing aging, preventing disease, weight loss and better thinking. It works through autophagy, mTOR, mitochondria and more.

3. Doctors have seen fasting reverse chronic disease, brain disorders and aging. Their results show its potential.

Issues Surrounding the Subject Matter

1. How might intermittent fasting and metabolic switching impact your health goals? What benefits are you most interested in exploring?

2. What challenges do you foresee in implementing an intermittent fasting routine? How might you adapt fasting strategies to fit your lifestyle?

3. How might intermittent fasting help counteract some of the metabolic dysfunction in modern diets? Could it play a role in preventing chronic diseases that are epidemic today?

Goals

1. Develop a sustainable intermittent fasting practice. Find the routine and frequency that works for your needs and lifestyle.

2. Enhance metabolic flexibility. Cycle between burning glucose and ketones. This means periods of fasting and feeding on a wholesome diet. It leads to weight loss, mental clarity, increased energy and more.

3. Slow or reverse aging. Intermittent fasting activates anti-aging pathways. It stimulates cellular repair, optimizes mitochondria, clears damage, and promotes regeneration. While aging is inevitable, we can extend health spans and wellbeing. Fasting offers a practical tool for longevity and quality of life. Live up to the term Age Young.

Action Steps

1. Start an overnight fast:
   a. Stop eating by 8pm and don't have your first meal until 12pm the next day. This provides you a 14-16 hour fasted window to start generating some of the benefits described, like autophagy, ketosis and hormesis. You can do this 3 times per week to begin. Build up as your body adapts.

2. Focus your diet on fasting-friendly foods:
   a. Meals of non-starchy veggies, healthy fats (avocados, nuts), protein (fatty fish, eggs, grass-fed meat)
   b. Limit sugar, grains, snacking
   c. Stay in fat-burning mode during feeding windows

3. Increase challenges over time:
   a. Start with 12-16 hour fasts, work up to 24 hour 2 times/week, 36-42 hour 1 time/month
   b. Cold exposure: ice baths, cryotherapy
   c. Intense exercise
   d. Reduce alcohol
   e. Improve stress management

Checklist

1. Types of fasts to experiment with:
   a. 12-16 hour overnight fast (stop eating at 8pm, resume at 8-12am)
   b. 24 hour fast 1-2 times per week (dinner-to-dinner)
   c. 36-42 hour fast 1-2 times per month (dinner-to-breakfast)

2. Ways to enhance metabolic flexibility:
   a. Practice intermittent fasting 3-4 times per week (12-16 hours to start)

b. Focus meals on non-starchy veggies, healthy fats, and protein
c. Limit excess sugar, refined grains and excess snacking

3. Support mitochondria and activate hormesis:
    a. Eat a diet high in antioxidants like leafy greens, colorful veggies and berries
    b. Meet protein needs to maintain muscle mass (aim for 20-30g with each meal)
    c. Stay active and exercise consistently including resistance training

Ch 4: Fasting a Woman's Way

Summary

Bridget was a successful career woman juggling life as a 40-year-old executive and mother of two teens. Her nonstop schedule left her constantly stressed, but her intense exercise routine was always her escape. As she moved into her early 40s though, Bridget's body started rebelling - strange symptoms like unexplained weight gain, frequent injuries, and unusual fatigue began preventing her regular workouts.

On a friend's suggestion, Bridget decided to try intermittent fasting as an alternative health booster. She quickly became hooked on the benefits like improved focus, energy, and inner calm. After six months of fasting, however, Bridget started experiencing troubling symptoms like heart palpitations, anxiety attacks, insomnia, and hair loss. Alarmed, she saw her doctor, who advised her to stop intermittent fasting, especially for women.

Her friend then recommended Bridget follow intermittent fasting guidelines tailored specifically for women and their monthly hormonal fluctuations. That's when Bridget realized her mistake - she hadn't accounted for how her own hormone cycle impacted her body's fasting response. By modifying her fasting schedule to match her menstrual cycle, the adverse symptoms disappeared within a month.

Unlike men, who have a steady hormone profile, women's hormones like estrogen, progesterone and testosterone rise and fall each month. These fluctuations shape a woman's moods, sleep quality, energy levels, and motivation over the course of her cycle. But most women never learn how their hormones change monthly or how to adapt habits like diet, exercise, and scheduling accordingly. By understanding her hormonal rhythms, Bridget learned how to tailor fasting to optimize her hormone health and feel her best.

A woman's hormonal health depends on a delicate dance between estrogen, progesterone, testosterone and other key players like thyroid hormone, cortisol, insulin and oxytocin. When one hormone falls out of step, it creates a domino effect on the others. For example, prolonged stress can increase cortisol, which then spikes insulin and depresses sex hormones like estrogen. Similarly, insulin resistance or a high-sugar, processed carb diet can shoot insulin levels up, impacting the rest of the hormonal system.

On the flip side, oxytocin, the "love hormone," lowers cortisol, helping balance blood sugar and support healthy sex hormone levels. Doing relaxing, pleasurable things like massage, sex, meditation or working out causes oxytocin release, which chills us out. Keeping cortisol and insulin in check is essential for women to maintain hormonal balance and healthy weight.

Hormonal health also relies on the liver, which processes excess estrogen for elimination. When the liver is sluggish from inflammation, toxins or fatty buildup, it can't properly metabolize hormones, which then recirculate in the body. This imbalance leads to issues like PMS, irregular periods, mood changes and endometriosis.

Stress also hits women's hormones harder for evolutionary reasons. In primitive days, stress meant imminent danger requiring a fight-or-flight reaction for survival. For men who hunted, this response was useful. But for women who nurtured children, chronically high cortisol from constant stress was counterproductive. Nowadays, stress is mostly psychological but still creates the same hormonal havoc for women.

Taking good care of ourselves through stress management, healthy eating, exercise, quality sleep and community support helps keep female hormones balanced. Some natural therapies like seed cycling with flax and pumpkin seeds to nourish estrogen and progesterone, fertility massage, and acupuncture can also bring hormones into alignment. When hormones are balanced and your body is working optimally, intermittent fasting can then work in synergy to provide even more health perks. But without addressing underlying issues first, fasting alone may not lead to lasting success and in some cases could make hormonal problems worse.

The bottom line is that hormonal health is critical for a woman's wellbeing and happiness. An approach that supports women's unique ever-changing hormone needs through education and the right tools can help us thrive. By understanding our bodies, hormones, minds and cycles, we can tap into our power and live in rhythm with our innate wisdom. This holistic self-care approach rewards women with balance, vitality and longevity. With patience and practice, every woman can achieve optimal health by learning to fast in a way that fits her feminine design.

Proper nutrition is the foundation for balanced hormones. An anti-inflammatory diet low in sugar, processed carbs and vegetable oils, but high in healthy fats, clean proteins and fiber, helps stabilize blood sugar, promote fat burning and detoxification. Key supplements like magnesium, B vitamins, vitamin D and turmeric also support hormonal balance and liver health. Adaptogens like ashwagandha, maca and licorice root help regulate the HPA axis (The HPA axis refers to the hypothalamic-pituitary-adrenal axis, which is a major part of the neuroendocrine system) that controls the stress response and other important body processes. It works through a negative feedback loop between the hypothalamus, pituitary gland, and adrenal glands. When the hypothalamus senses stress, it releases CRH hormone. CRH triggers the pituitary to release ACTH hormone. ACTH causes the adrenals to produce cortisol. Cortisol is the "stress hormone" that mobilizes resources to deal with threats. When cortisol gets too high, it signals the HPA axis to slow down cortisol production and return the body to balance.

Sleep also significantly impacts female hormones. During sleep, the body works to repair cells, rebalance hormones and clear toxins. Skimping on sleep increases cortisol and drives cravings. Aim for 7-9 hours nightly in a cool, dark room without electronics. Keeping a steady sleep/wake cycle also helps.

Exercise provides both physical and mental benefits for hormonal health. A balanced routine of cardio, strength training, and stretching reduces inflammation and excess fat tissue, which mess with hormones. But overdoing it also spikes cortisol and can disrupt reproduction. Moderation and rest days are key. Walking, yoga and meditation are gentle yet effective ways to release oxytocin and stay active without overtaxing your body.

Personal relationships help women feel connected and calm, lowering stress hormones. Close female friendships provide empathy, advice and understanding for balancing hormones and life. Spending time with loved ones releases oxytocin, counteracting cortisol. Love and intimacy in a committed partnership with a caring partner also nourishes hormonal health and happiness. Community involvement through volunteering, religious or social groups creates meaning and purpose.

For some women, medical support may be needed for hormonal issues. Thyroid medication, hormone therapy for menopause, and other treatments for conditions like PCOS or endometriosis can address root causes directly. However, natural remedies and lifestyle changes should be attempted first when possible, under a trusted doctor's guidance. Pharmaceutical medicine has its place but shouldn't replace common sense self-care.

Nowadays, women juggle caring for partners, kids, parents along with their own work. But sacrificing self-care for these endless demands leads to hormonal havoc and lack of joy. When women nurture balanced living through health, community, meaningful work, relationships and personal growth, hormones find harmony. By reducing stress responses and inflammatory lifestyle factors, the body can devote resources toward vitality and longevity rather than disruption. Despite life's challenges, women must remember their hormonal health and happiness matter. With practice, patience and proper support, each woman can find her unique formula to thrive. She just needs to learn how to fast like a girl.

Lessons

1. A woman's hormones fluctuate monthly, requiring tailored self-care. First, she must understand her unique hormonal changes to support her health. Hormones interact delicately, and an imbalance in one affects the others. She should monitor her hormonal fluctuations and meet their needs through her lifestyle.

2. Lifestyle significantly impacts female hormones. Chronic stress, a lack of self-care, and unhealthy habits disrupt hormonal balance. However, nutrition, exercise, rest, and relationships that nourish wellbeing cultivate hormonal harmony. She must nurture herself through balanced and sustainable life practices.

3. She should adjust intermittent fasting to her menstrual cycle. While men may fast similarly daily, she needs to tailor her fasting to complement her monthly hormonal shifts. She must fast in a way that provides benefits without consequences by suiting her body's fluctuations.

Issues Surrounding the Subject Matter

1. How well do you know your hormonal changes each month? Do you understand how your hormones interact? Gain awareness about your cycle for your health. How will you increase your knowledge of your patterns?

2. Do you practice self-care for hormonal health? If not, what prevents sustainable care? Your habits impact your daily balance. How will you choose nutrition, movement, stress relief, rest, and socializing? Make time for yourself.

3. Have you considered matching fasts to your cycle? Rather than one plan, adjust to complement hormonal changes monthly. How will you track how fasting affects you and design a tailored regimen? Start gradually and be flexible. Speak to your doctor before extending your fast.

Goals

1. Gain knowledge of your hormonal patterns and monthly changes. Track your cycle and symptoms, learn about monthly hormone fluctuations, and test levels if needed. Increase awareness of your feminine health needs. Understand how your hormones interact to support balance and wellbeing. Build capacity to thrive.

2. Develop self-care habits for hormonal harmony. Focus on balanced nutrition, movement, stress management, rest, limiting unhealthy choices, and social connection. Overcome obstacles to sustainable health. Cultivate gradual lifestyle balance for vitality, clarity, and calm. Choose to listen within for wisdom.

3. Determine tailored fasts for your monthly hormonal changes. Rather than one-size-fits-all, adjust periods to complement your cycle phases. Journal about how different fasts affect you. Gain insight into what supports your wellbeing. Your fast suits your needs. Apply selectively to experience benefits without

adverse effects. Your power comes from caring for your natural design. Start slow, be patient, and find your own way.

Action Steps

1. Learn about your hormonal cycles.
   - Understand how estrogen, progesterone and testosterone fluctuate
   - Know which phases of your cycle match with which hormones

2. Improve diet, sleep, exercise.
   - Eat anti-inflammatory foods
   - Get 7-9 hours of sleep per night
   - Do a mix of cardio, weights and yoga

3. Seek medical advice if needed.
   - Consult doctor for thyroid dysfunction
   - Get treatment for PCOS or menopause symptoms

Checklist

1. Gain awareness of your hormonal patterns and monthly cycle.
   a. Track your menstrual cycle and symptoms daily to understand your hormonal fluctuations.

b. Research hormone changes each month to learn the natural rhythms.

c. Test your hormonal levels with your doctor if needed to increase knowledge of your needs.

d. Understand how your hormones interact to influence your experience and support balance. Build capacity to thrive through self-wisdom.

2. Develop lifestyle habits that cultivate hormonal harmony.

a. Focus on balanced nutrition, movement, stress relief, rest, limiting unhealthy choices, and social connection.

b. Identify obstacles preventing sustainable health habits and solutions to overcome them. Get support if needed.

c. Make gradual changes day by day for vitality, clarity, and calm. Listen within for guidance.

3. Determine tailored intermittent fasting periods that complement your monthly cycle.

a. Track how different fasts affect you during hormonal changes each month. Journal your experiences.

b. Start with shorter fasts, building up as suits your needs. Be flexible.

c. 14–16 hour or longer fasts may serve better around ovulation or menstruation.

PART 2: The Art of Fasting Like a Girl

Ch 5: Build a Fasting Lifestyle Unique to You

Summary

The conventional approach to healthcare often takes a one-size-fits-all approach, prescribing the same treatments to every patient with a given diagnosis. This has left many feeling frustrated with the generic solutions that fail to address their unique health conditions. In response, the concept of personalized or functional medicine has gained popularity, building customized health programs that help individuals function at their personal best.

The book cites high blood pressure as an example. While medication may help some, the underlying cause necessitating it can vary greatly between individuals. Seeking more tailored solutions, millions are now turning to functional medicine practitioners to uncover why their particular health crisis began and what can be done to resolve it.

Central to this functional approach is the concept of "n-of-1 trials," where patients actively participate in deciding their treatment plans with their doctor. This has been shown to improve outcomes for those with chronic illnesses as patients gain greater understanding and control over their health.

Dr Pelz also argues fasting too should be an individualized journey to find what works best for each person - determining optimal fasting lengths and how to incorporate it into one's lifestyle. Most diets are rigid, but fasting can be flexible and customized according to one's needs, events, and schedule. This segment introduces the idea of "the four pillars" to guide people starting a fasting lifestyle.

PILLAR #1: Identify Your Goals

Determine your aims—weight loss, hormonal balance, or alleviating a condition—and choose fasts accordingly.

Lose weight
Women often lose weight slower with fasting than men. Periodic 36+ hour fasts can accelerate female weight loss. Be patient and persistent.

Balance hormones
Fasting regulates insulin, balances sex hormones, and resolves issues like PCOS, infertility, and menopause symptoms. Follow protocols for optimal results and be patient; hormonal issues lasting years can take months of consistent fasting to fully resolve.

Alleviate conditions

Fasting dramatically improves conditions like autoimmunity, cancer, diabetes, mood disorders, and brain disorders. Follow specific fasting protocols as treatment plans and use fasting as a first-line therapy.

PILLAR #2: Vary Your Fasting Lengths

Discover your optimal daily fasting window, often an 8-hour period like 11 a.m.–7p.m.

Next, vary fasts by incorporating different lengths of intermittent fasts or occasional 24- to 36-hour fasts. This provides three key benefits:

Avoid plateaus

Varying fasts keeps the body adapting, preventing complacency that can stall progress. Occasional fasting variations provide hormetic stress.

Honor hormonal surges

Shorten fasts when hormones peak premenstrually and at ovulation. Lengthen fasts when hormones are low, like after a period starts and post-ovulation. Tune fasts to hormonal fluctuations.

Allow flexibility

Fasting variation accommodates life changes, sustaining success over the long term. Enjoy parties by fasting earlier and indulging later. On vacation, relax, fast, and enjoy new foods.

Troubleshoot symptoms

Monitor symptoms as feedback on fasting's alignment with hormones. Weight gain, lost periods, or the return of old issues indicate fasts aren't matching cycle phases. Refine your approach through trial and error.

Support success habits

Build community connections for support, encouragement, and accountability. Gather friends to fast, exercise, and heal together. This social support provides an oxytocin burst that amplifies fasting's benefits. Replace isolation with communal support for greater results.

PILLAR #3: Vary Your Food Choices

Eating diverse foods, not the same ones repeatedly, optimizes health. The female body thrives on variety. Repeated foods strengthen craving-driving gut microbes. Each new food nourishes new microbes, influencing food preferences.

Cravings are often dictated by taste buds and stubborn microbes. Give in to cravings, and those microbes flourish. Varying food choices transforms the gut terrain, killing craving-causing microbes. As they die off, so do the cravings.

Studies show the gut microbiome impacts food preferences. For instance, candida drives sugar cravings. Don't let stubborn microbes control your choices. Diversify foods to gain control.

Recommended variations are ketobiotic and hormone-feasting diets - focusing on low carbs, healthy fats, protein, greens, and foods targeting each menstrual phase.

PILLAR #4: Surround Yourself with a Supportive Community

Building a supportive community is so important when incorporating fasting into a lifestyle. Surrounding yourself with positive people who encourage you makes a huge difference. The oxytocin burst that comes from social connections can really amplify fasting's benefits. As women, we tend to thrive when we have a community behind us. Getting together with friends to fast, exercise, and heal replaces isolation with real human bonds. Having people lift you up and make optimal health fun turns healing into a shared experience.

A community also holds you accountable to stick with the lifestyle changes. Going through the ups and downs together makes it so much easier to troubleshoot challenges and refine your approach. That social support is truly key for long-term success.

In summary, the four pillars that create an optimal fasting lifestyle for a woman are: identify your goals and choose fasts that align; vary fasting lengths to prevent plateaus, sync with your cycle, and allow flexibility; vary food choices to nourish gut bugs and transform cravings; and surround yourself with a supportive community to get that oxytocin flowing and accelerate healing. Follow those pillars, and you can craft a fasting lifestyle for amazing health.

Now, as you make fasting your lifestyle, relationships should stay a priority. Positive, supportive connections are so vital for health - like the oxytocin you get from loved ones. Fasting should still let you enjoy meals together with family and friends. With some flexibility, you can shape a fasting lifestyle that feeds your relationships while optimizing your health.

To fit fasting into family life, customize your approach. Your fasting windows can adapt around making the kids' lunches or sitting down to dinner together. Varying your fasts and food choices lets fasting work within the demands of any relationship.

Just like with your relationships, you can tailor fasting to fit any schedule or lifestyle. For example, an actress shooting overnight was able to use intermittent fasting and meal timing strategically to restore her energy and stamina despite an erratic sleep routine.

Your fasting windows can adapt to your activity levels too. Athletes might widen eating windows on heavy training days while doing longer fasts on lower mileage days. If you have a mentally demanding job, you can structure fasts to optimize energy and performance for when you need it most.

Let's look at an inspirational story about a woman who used fasting's flexibility to totally transform her health. Weighing close to 100 pounds overweight with uncontrolled diabetes, her doctor had no advice besides lose weight and watch your sugar. Taking charge of her own health, she researched and taught herself intermittent fasting, steadily losing weight and reducing medications. Adding the Whole30 diet sped up her results. She then tried out ketogenic eating for the ultra low-carb approach. After just 9 months of educated fasting lifestyle adjustments, she had lost 70 pounds and regained control over her health.

This shows that by educating yourself online and creating personalized fasting protocols, you can overcome even poor medical advice. Doctors may not know about lifestyle solutions, but you have the power to transform your health through research and strategic fasting.

Remember, your fasting lifestyle as a woman will look very different from a man's because of hormonal differences. Comparing yourself will only lead to frustration. Stay positive and tune your fasts to honor your unique female hormonal flows. Fasting feedback helps you learn - there is no failure, only growth. Any stumble just represents your neurons getting smarter.

With your hormone cycles always in the driver's seat, use fasting's flexibility to adapt to relationships, schedules, activity levels, and anything else life throws your way. Reread the principles during any setbacks or plateaus. Stick with it and fasting will become an effortless lifestyle habit.

Lessons

1. When it comes to fasting, there's no one-size-fits-all approach. What works for one person may not work for another. It's important to personalize fasting plans based on individual goals, hormone cycles, schedules, lifestyles and so on. Customization is key.

2. To keep seeing results, it's helpful to switch things up with fasting durations and food choices. Sticking to the same routine day after day can backfire. Variety prevents the body and mind from hitting a plateau.

3. Having a supportive community makes the fasting journey much easier and more enjoyable. There's power in embarking on a health goal together with others. It provides accountability, motivation and fun. Tackling it solo can be challenging.

Issues Surrounding the Subject Matter

1. How might you customize your fasting plan to align with your unique health goals, schedule and lifestyle? What specific adjustments could help optimize your results?

2. In what ways could you vary your fasting protocols or diet to keep your body adapting? Are there certain

routines you've fallen into that may be holding you back?

3. Who might you connect with to build a supportive fasting community? How could you encourage and uplift each other throughout the process? What benefits might you all gain by embarking on this journey together?

Goals

1. One goal can be to lose weight at a steady pace that's sustainable - nothing too extreme or crash-diet-like. This may involve playing around with different fasting durations and meal timing to see what works best for your unique body and lifestyle. Patience and consistency become so important.

2. Another goal for some is getting hormones like insulin, estrogen and testosterone into balance. Carefully designed fasting protocols can help get them in harmony over time. Paying attention to your monthly cycle and syncing up fasts accordingly may further help things along. Progress happens gradually, so sticking with it through the ups and downs is key.

3. Others may be drawn to fasting to find relief from conditions like autoimmunity, diabetes or mood stuff. Following specific fasting regimens as treatment plans, while also using fasting as a first resort, could provide

noticeable improvements. Combining fasting with other positive lifestyle tweaks may further enhance your results and overall wellbeing.

Action Steps

1. Take a look at your particular health goals - whether it's hormone balance, weight loss, or something else - and design a customized fasting routine to match. For example, longer fasts like 36+ hours can provide an extra boost for female weight loss.

2. Switch up that daily fasting schedule periodically to keep your body adapting. If 16:8 is your normal, try alternating 14, 16, and 18 hour fasts. Keeping it varied helps prevent plateaus.

3. Get yourself an accountability buddy or community to join you on the journey! Connect with fellow fasters online or plan some walk fasts with friends. Having support and company makes the whole process more doable and enjoyable.

Checklist

1. Customize your own fasting plan based on your specific goals, hormone cycles, schedule, lifestyle - the whole enchilada. Tailor it to fit you and your unique needs.

2. Switch up your fasting routines periodically - keep your body guessing. Vary the lengths of your fasts and the types of foods you eat to keep adapting. Don't get stuck in a plateau.

3. Build yourself a solid support network. Connect with positive peeps who can provide accountability, encouragement and community. Having some cheerleaders makes the journey way more enjoyable.

Ch 6: The Power of Belief

Summary

FOOD PRINCIPLE #1-INGREDIENTS MATTER

In this chapter, Dr Mindy Pelz highlights the importance of healthy fats for hormone production, particularly cholesterol. Cholesterol provides the building blocks to manufacture estrogen, progesterone and testosterone. Foods naturally high in cholesterol like egg yolks, shellfish, organ meats and fatty fish are advised to support hormone synthesis.

She also goes on to stress how cholesterol has been wrongfully vilified, when in fact the body needs ample cholesterol to produce sex hormones. As covered, there are two main types - HDL or "good" cholesterol and LDL or "bad" cholesterol. HDL carries cholesterol to tissues to synthesize hormones and should be elevated. LDL contributes to plaque buildup in arteries and should be reduced.

Dr Pelz then recommends a diet moderate in healthy fats and cholesterol along with regular exercise to raise HDL and lower LDL cholesterol. As noted, certain foods can shift cholesterol ratios favorably - avocados, nuts, olive oil, salmon, and green tea all raise HDL. Additionally, soluble fiber from oats, fruits and vegetables lowers LDL cholesterol levels to balance the profile.

In addition to cholesterol, adequate protein intake enables the body to manufacture hormones. As explained, grass-fed meats, pasture-raised poultry, wild caught fish, eggs, bone broth and fermented dairy provide amino acids to construct hormones. Nuts, seeds and legumes also provide plant-based proteins. Additionally, protein further helps stabilize blood sugar to support hormonal equilibrium.

At this juncture, it must be pointed out that a woman's body innately elevates HDL cholesterol mid-cycle when estrogen production peaks. Consequently, women's cholesterol profiles naturally shift throughout the menstrual cycle to meet hormonal requirements. This biological mechanism supports strategically eating cholesterol-rich foods in sync with menstrual phases.

The guidance indicates women should cycle their carbohydrate intake over the course of their menstrual cycle. During the follicular phase after menstruation, consuming fewer carbs enhances insulin sensitivity to optimize estrogen production. Higher carb foods can be added back leading up to menstruation when progesterone is dominant to help induce shedding of the uterine lining. Avoiding blood sugar spikes when estrogen peaks after menstruation enhances hormonal balance.

Additional tips are provided for balancing hormones through strategic nutrition. Getting adequate fiber helps eliminate excess estrogen so it doesn't recirculate through enterohepatic circulation. Cruciferous vegetables like broccoli boost estrogen detoxification in the liver to prevent buildup. Probiotic foods spur healthy gut flora to improve estrogen metabolism. Stress-reducing nutrients like magnesium and B vitamins promote cortisol regulation.

With hormone levels declining with age, it underscores the importance of eating to support the endocrine system. Nutrients that boost energy metabolism and mitochondrial function may help counteract waning hormone output. As noted, coenzyme Q10, alpha-lipoic acid, carnitine and sulforaphane support cellular energy pathways involved in hormone creation.

A variety of foods can support healthy estrogen production in the body. Good fats like those found in oils such as olive, flaxseed and sesame seed, as well as avocados, provide phytoestrogens that can lower the risk of conditions like osteoporosis, heart disease, breast cancer and menopausal symptoms. Seeds and nuts including Brazil nuts, almonds, cashews, peanuts, pine nuts, pumpkin seeds, sunflower seeds, walnuts and sesame seeds also contain helpful phytoestrogens. Legumes like peas, chickpeas, soybeans, beans, lentils and black-eyed peas are additional sources. Fruits and vegetables including sprouts, cabbage, spinach, onions, garlic, zucchini, broccoli, cauliflower, strawberries, blueberries and cranberries boost estrogen too. Healthy estrogen levels promote normal ovulation. Estrogen is especially important in the days before ovulation, so consuming these phytoestrogen-rich foods is key.

Progesterone is another hormone influenced by diet. Progesterone prefers higher blood sugar than estrogen. Before a period, cravings for carbohydrates are common as the body naturally elevates blood sugar to ensure adequate progesterone production. Monitoring blood sugar levels will reveal they increase just before the menstrual period. Foods like potatoes and other root vegetables, cruciferous vegetables, tropical and citrus fruits, and seeds raise blood sugar and provide glucose for progesterone synthesis. However, pairing these foods with inflammatory oils can negate benefits. A balanced approach supports optimal hormonal health.

Building muscle and maintaining a healthy microbiome through diet are important for overall health. Muscle strength provides metabolic, bone, mental and longevity benefits for women. Building muscle requires eating adequate protein to stimulate the mTOR cellular pathway. Meanwhile, fasting stimulates autophagy. Therefore, strategically combining fasting periods with protein consumption can support muscle growth and fat loss.

Choosing quality protein sources is key. Animal proteins offer all 9 essential amino acids, whereas plants have incomplete amino acid profiles. The amino acids leucine, isoleucine and valine are especially important for muscle building. Leucine-rich animal protein sources include chicken, beef, pork, fish, eggs and dairy. Plant sources with leucine are pumpkin seeds, navy beans and tofu. Vegetarians often supplement with amino acids. When selecting animal or plant proteins, choose organic, non-GMO options to avoid hormones or pesticides.

30 grams of protein per meal optimally triggers mTOR for muscle growth. Amino acid sensing ability declines after age 40, so sufficient protein becomes even more important for preserving strength and function.

The gut microbiome also influences health. Gut bacteria support neurotransmitter synthesis, estrogen metabolism, immunity and sleep. Diets high in processed foods and bad fats damage gut flora. But probiotics, prebiotics and polyphenols repair microbiome health rapidly.

Probiotics contain live bacteria that produce vitamins, reduce inflammation and benefit immunity. Fermented foods like sauerkraut, kimchi, pickles, yogurt and kefir provide probiotics. Each imparts unique advantages - kefir boosts cholesterol, blood pressure and antioxidants while fermented scallions in kimchi increase viral immunity.

Prebiotics contain fiber that feeds microbiome growth. Polyphenols in plants act as antioxidants and nourish gut bacteria. A diet rich in the three Ps supports optimal hormonal health by assisting estrogen breakdown and promoting excretion. Food variety also matters for microbiome diversity.

Focusing on quality sources of muscle-building protein while also consuming probiotic, prebiotic and polyphenol-rich foods to support microbiome health allows women to feel their best both physically and mentally while aging gracefully. Combining fasting and strategic eating can help create metabolic flexibility for lifelong health.

Prebiotics and polyphenols also support microbiome health. Prebiotics contain fiber that feeds the good gut bacteria. Important prebiotic foods include chicory, dandelion, konjac and burdock root, onions, Jerusalem artichoke, garlic, leeks, asparagus, beans, chickpeas, split peas, cashews and pistachios. Consuming prebiotics helps the beneficial bacteria thrive just as you would feed a pet to keep it alive. (only difference is that this pet will help keep your body in a good, healthy shape)

Polyphenols are plant compounds with antioxidant effects that create an optimal environment for microbiome diversity. Polyphenol-rich foods like artichokes, broccoli, Brussels sprouts, cloves, saffron, oregano, rosemary, thyme, basil, cinnamon, cumin, curry, dark chocolate, olives, parsley, red wine and shallots nourish gut flora. Focusing on quality is key - low alcohol, sustainable wines and dark chocolate with over 70% cacao provide more polyphenols than commercial varieties.

Polyphenols offer additional benefits like regulating blood pressure, reducing inflammation, protecting the brain and lowering blood sugar. Herbs and spices are surprisingly high in polyphenols - cloves, for example, support the liver and blood sugar.

As taste buds change with fasting, being intentional about consuming hormone-supporting, muscle-building and microbiome-feeding foods becomes even more important. Appetite and cravings may decrease, so we must deliberately include foods that provide phytoestrogens, amino acids, probiotics, prebiotics and polyphenols.

A diet rich in fermented foods, fiber-filled plants, antioxidant-packed spices, high-quality chocolate and wine, beans, nuts, seeds, whole grains, fruits and vegetables gives the microbiome the diversity it needs for optimal hormonal health. Supporting healthy estrogen metabolism and excretion through strategic eating enables women to feel their best while fasting.

FOOD PRINCIPLE #2-GLYCEMIC LOAD MATTERS

The glycemic index ranks foods from 1 to 100 based on their impact on blood sugar levels. Foods closer to 100 spike blood sugar more than foods closer to 1. Monitoring blood sugar provides insight into metabolic health. While many factors influence blood sugar, the macronutrient composition of foods has the greatest effect. Understanding how carbohydrates, proteins and fats uniquely affect blood sugar enables optimization of dietary choices for metabolic flexibility, hormonal balance and fat-burning.

Carbohydrates strongly influence blood sugar and come in simple or complex forms. Simple carbs like cookies and cereals made by processed means spike blood sugar rapidly due to lack of fiber. This can overload the body's ability to assimilate sugar, causing storage in the liver and fat cells. Complex carbs made by nature like fruits and vegetables have fiber that slows sugar absorption, allowing gradual cellular uptake and preventing fat storage. Simple carbs provide empty calories without health benefits, while complex carbs support muscles, hormones and microbiome. To manage blood sugar, focus on net carbs by subtracting fiber from total carbs.

Protein also raises blood sugar but more moderately than carbs. First, it breaks down into glucose slowly. Second, protein slows carbohydrate absorption, preventing blood sugar spikes. This makes pairing carbs with protein helpful. Finally, protein increases satiety. For women beginning to fast, protein rich snacks can ease hunger, boost energy and smooth transitions between fasting and eating. However, excessive protein beyond 75 grams daily can also spike blood sugar and hinder fat-burning, so moderation is key.

Fat provides the most blood sugar benefits. It stabilizes blood sugar, decreases appetite and does not convert to glucose. But quality matters - good fats nourish cells while bad fats inflame them. Good fats repair cell membranes for proper nutrient assimilation and toxin release. Bad fats damage membranes, preventing cellular health. With the vital impact of good fats recognized, high-quality, fat-rich food options are now widely available.

Understanding how carbohydrates, proteins and fats uniquely influence blood sugar and insulin allows optimization of meal composition for metabolic health. Pairing complex carbs with protein, moderating protein intake and focusing on good fats enables women to succeed with fasting. Stable blood sugar and insulin levels spur fat-burning, boost energy, accelerate weight loss and support hormonal balance. Making informed macro choices empowers women to feel their best while fasting.

FOOD PRINCIPLE #3-DIVERSITY MATTERS

Diversifying food choices supports microbiome health but is often overlooked. Different foods contain unique nutrients that feed different gut bacteria. For example, Prevotella thrives on carbohydrates, bifidobacteria prefer fiber, and Bacteroidetes grow best with certain fats. When food variety is limited, microbial diversity suffers. To cultivate microbiome diversity, make an effort to consume at least 200 different foods monthly including carbohydrates, proteins and fats. Only count complex, natural carbs, not simple ones like cookies. Spices can substantially boost diversity. To remember variety, play the food diversity score game by tracking different foods eaten weekly. Spice options like cardamom, cumin, onion powder, garlic powder, rosemary, thyme, saffron, nutmeg, cinnamon and cloves add diversity. Consciously varying diet improves microbial fitness and hormone balance.

FOOD PRINCIPLE #4-CYCLING MATTERS

Varying food choices over time supports hormones like cycling diet feeds microbes. Women's menstrual cycles create a natural pattern for cycling nutrition. During the follicular phase when estrogen surges, a ketobiotic diet thrives. Then in the luteal phase when progesterone rises, complex carbs in hormone feasting foods benefit. Postmenopausal women or those without cycles can use a 30-day reset to ensure proper food and fasting cycles monthly. Though complex, cycling food and fasting with hormonal fluctuations magnifies feminine natural powers. Once hormonal patterns are understood, effortlessly matching nutritional choices becomes fun, easy and empowering.

Two optimal eating styles for women are ketobiotic and hormone feasting. Ketobiotic regulates blood sugar for estrogen while hormone feasting raises glucose for progesterone. Together they encompass the four food principles and mimic ancestral feast/famine cycles timed to hormones.

Ketobiotic is a women-focused ketogenic approach. It limits carbs to 50 net grams daily from vegetables and greens. Protein is capped at 75 grams of clean sources per day. Over 60% of food comes from healthy fats. Benefits include accelerated fat-burning, estrogen support, increased vegetables, liver and gut detoxification, and brain-fueling ketones.

Hormone feasting days provide more carbs up to 150 net grams daily to elevate progesterone. Carbs come from nature's sources like root vegetables and fruits. Protein is lowered to 50 grams while healthy fats are encouraged. This diet boosts feel-good neurotransmitters, cognition, sleep and microbiome diversity. It purposefully increases blood sugar, which may pause ketosis temporarily.

Ketobiotic works best in the early follicular phase when estrogen is low, keeping insulin low too. Hormone feasting is optimal around ovulation and the week before menstruation when progesterone needs a glucose boost. Despite higher carb intake, this cyclic rhythm aligns with hormones to enable effortless weight loss.

For women without cycles, a monthly reset alternating between ketobiotic and hormone feasting days provides the same benefits. Cycling nutrition mimics ancestral feast/famine patterns. When hormones are peaking, feed them with hormone feasting. When hormones are low, practice ketobiotic eating. Listen to your body's innate wisdom.

With these two dietary frameworks, women now have a customizable approach to eating that maximizes hormones, muscles, microbiome and metabolism in alignment with feminine needs. Combining strategic fasting with ketobiotic and hormone feasting days allows women to thrive, prevent disease and age vibrantly. Hormonal balance and overall health flourish when women eat and fast according to nature's divine design.

Lessons

1. Quality ingredients like healthy fats and proteins are vital for hormone production. Foods high in good cholesterol like eggs and seafood provide building blocks for estrogen and testosterone. Grass-fed meats supply amino acids to manufacture hormones.

2. Balancing blood sugar is crucial through mindful carb intake and pairing carbs with protein and good fats. This prevents insulin spikes that can lead to fat storage and hormonal issues. Monitoring glycemic response provides insight for optimizing meals.

3. Diversifying food choices regularly feeds different gut bacteria for microbiome health. Making an effort to consume at least 200 various natural foods monthly boosts microbial diversity which supports hormones.

Issues surrounding the subject matter

1. As discussed, high-quality fats and proteins provide the raw materials for hormone synthesis. What changes could readers make to their diets to increase intake of these beneficial nutrients?

2. Managing blood sugar spikes is highlighted as being important for metabolic health and weight management. What insights did readers gain from the summary about how different macros impact blood sugar? What strategies might readers implement?

3. Microbiome diversity is linked to improved hormone balance. How could readers boost the variety of natural, complex carbs, proteins and fats in their diets to better feed their gut bacteria? What goal might readers set for increasing their dietary diversity?

Goals

1. You could set a goal to eat 3-4 servings per week of cholesterol-rich foods like eggs, shellfish, liver or fatty fish to support hormone production.

2. It also may be good to aim to balance their carb intake by pairing carbs with protein or fat at each meal to prevent blood sugar spikes. They could track their post-meal blood sugar response.

3. Alternatively you might strive to consume at least 25 different natural foods per week to build microbiome diversity. They could play the food diversity score game to increase variety.

Action Steps

1. Readers can increase consumption of healthy fats like olive oil, avocados, and nuts which provide building blocks for hormone synthesis. For example, the summary mentioned avocados raise HDL cholesterol.

2. Readers should pair carbs with protein or fat to stabilize blood sugar. For instance, the summary suggested combining potatoes or fruit with good fats rather than inflammatory oils.

3. Readers can diversify food choices by intentionally incorporating new spices mentioned in the summary like cardamom, saffron and turmeric which provide polyphenols.

Checklist

1. Increase intake of cholesterol-rich foods. Readers could check off eating 3 eggs per week or trying a new recipe with organ meats like liver.

2. Balance carbs with protein or fat. Readers could track pairing carbs with protein, fat or both at each meal and check off days they succeed in stabilizing blood sugar.

3. Boost food diversity. Readers could use a checklist to tally consumption of 30 different whole foods per week or 10 new herbs/spices monthly.

Ch 7: The Fasting Cycle

Summary

Dr. Mindy Pelz talks about a method called the Fasting Cycle that's designed to help women fast in a way that jives with their monthly menstrual cycle. The idea is to match up when and how long you fast with where you're at hormone-wise in your cycle.

The Fasting Cycle divides the menstrual cycle into three phases - Power Phase, Manifestation Phase, and Nurture Phase - with tailored fasting and diet recommendations for each one.

When a woman is in the Power Phase and estrogen levels are at their highest, she can try stretching out her fasts a little to give cellular regeneration a boost. Then when she hits the Manifestation Phase around ovulation, moderate fasting can help keep her hormones balanced. And during the Nurture Phase when progesterone peaks, gentle fasting paired with nourishing foods is recommended.

If she matches her fasting approach to each phase, she gets all the benefits without messing up her hormones, which can definitely happen if you are fasting too hard at the wrong time of the month. The 30-Day Fasting Reset gives women a pre-planned program to try out the Fasting Cycle method.

Dr. Pelz uses an example of a woman named Amy who lost her period from fasting without thinking about her cycle phase. But when she synced up her fasts with her Fasting Cycle, her menstrual cycle normalized and she was able to improve her fertility.

What this illustrates is that fasting can be awesome for women if it's tailored to their personal menstrual flow. Using a woman's Fasting Cycle allows her to tap into fasting's perks like cell rejuvenation, weight loss, and reproductive health support. It's about working cooperatively with the body's natural rhythms, not fighting against them. Fasting this way can help optimize a woman's hormones.

The Power Phase has two windows - days 1-10 and 16-19 - when sex hormone levels dip, making it ideal for longer fasts of 13-72 hours. During days 1-10, estrogen begins rising to trigger ovulation. Fasting helps lower insulin, which can inhibit estrogen if chronically elevated. Estrogen deficiency along with insulin excess can lead to issues like PCOS. Longer fasts stimulate autophagy, hence repairing tissues in the body including those of ovaries and the brain which govern hormones. Fasting also induces ketosis where efficient ketones fuel mitochondria. Together autophagy and ketosis optimize these hormonal control centers.

During days 16-19, sex hormones decline again after peaking mid-cycle. Another window opens for longer fasts to promote autophagy, burn fat, improve brain function, and enhance immunity without disrupting hormones. A ketobiotic diet with low carbs, high healthy fats, and moderate protein aligns well with longer fasts. Food choices like avocado, flax oil, sauerkraut, salad, and grass-fed steak provide good fats and proteins while stabilizing glucose and insulin.

The Manifestation Phase from days 11-15 has rapidly rising estrogen, testosterone, and progesterone. Here the healing focus shifts from hormone production to metabolism. Shorter fasts under 15 hours are recommended, as longer fasts can cause detox symptoms from toxins released during hormonal peaks. Supporting liver and gut function becomes paramount for metabolizing and excreting hormones.

Estrogen breakdown is especially crucial. Unmetabolized estrogen promotes cancers and symptoms like breast pain, sweating, and mood swings. Hormone feasting foods enhance detox capacity via compounds that improve bile flow, digestion, and nutrient absorption. Examples include cruciferous vegetables, leafy greens, berries, salmon, and fermented foods. Phthalate avoidance and stress management also enable optimal testosterone, which gives motivation and sex drive.

The Nurture Phase spans from day 20 until menstruation. Here the goal is nourishing rest without fasting or intense exercise which raises cortisol. Cortisol competes for resources with progesterone synthesis. Progesterone provides a sense of calm before shedding the uterine lining. Light exercise like walking and yoga along with starchy comfort foods support progesterone production. Sources like root vegetables, beans, rice, and fruit provide glucose while delivering nutrition. Saying "no" to excessive workloads also helps lower stressful cortisol spikes.

More Details on Each Phase:

The Power Phase's longer fasts spur autophagy, the cellular cleansing process that recycles damaged components. Autophagy selectively repairs tissues including the brain's hormonal control centers and ovarian follicles. Fasting also induces ketosis whereby efficient ketones synthesized from fat provide a steady fuel source for mitochondria. Ketones prevent spikes and drops in glucose that can tax hormonal organs. Their stable energy enables smoother hormonal rhythms.

During the Manifestation Phase, estrogen and testosterone surge. Now the liver and gut metabolize the heightened hormones while shorter fasts prevent release of toxins stored in fat cells that get mobilized by fasting. Hormone feasting foods enhance detoxification and excretion capacity through various actions:

- Improving bile flow to enable estrogen breakdown
- Stimulating digestion via stomach acid and pancreatic enzymes
- Enabling nutrient absorption like B12 and iron

- Providing compounds that upregulate detox genes or support detoxification pathways

Lifestyle factors like phthalate avoidance and stress management preserve testosterone since cortisol competes for its DHEA precursor.

Finally in the Nurture Phase, nourishing activities coupled with starchy comfort foods boost progesterone synthesis. Cortisol from fasting and excessive exercise inhibits progesterone. Lower intensity movement and glucose from starchy foods provide resources for elevated progesterone which helps shed the uterine lining during menses. Saying "no" to extra duties also prevents cortisol spikes from depleting progesterone levels.

The Fasting Cycle offers guidance to properly time fasts based on hormone changes. It assists female fasters sync longer fasts with optimal windows. The upcoming 30-Day Reset provides a proven step-by-step plan implementing this approach, pairing fast lengths and foods to each cycle phase.

Fasting can be addictive as benefits manifest, tempting continuous extended fasts. Yet fasting must align with menstrual patterns for balance. The Fasting Cycle framework leverages fasting's power while averting disruption.

When health falters, remember the body is wired to self-repair given the right conditions. Evaluate whether lifestyle choices support female physiology. The Fasting Cycle charts fasting duration across the menstrual cycle, allowing cellular renewal, fat incineration, and revival during prime times while providing sustenance during delicate phases. This empowers women to collaborate with hormones for better wellbeing.

To sum it all up, the Power Phase fasting and ketobiotic diet facilitate cellular cleansing and efficient mitochondrial fueling to optimize hormonal organs. The Manifestation Phase diet and lifestyle support hormone metabolism and detoxification. Finally, the Nurture Phase activities and food choices enable progesterone synthesis and calm. Tailoring the fasting approach and diet to each menstrual phase allows women to time restricted fasting periods for hormonal advantage while providing nourishment during delicate windows. Aligning with female physiology promotes hormonal health.

Lessons

1. Fasting can be super helpful for ladies if timed wisely with your monthly flow. Following a fasting plan tailored to your own hormone ups and downs enables you to optimize the bonuses like weight loss, cell rejuvenation, and reproductive health.

2. Customizing your fasting approach and diet to sync with each phase of your cycle is clutch. This allows you to tap into autophagy, ketosis, and fat burning during the prime times while giving your body nourishment during the delicate times.

3. Working with, not against your body's natural rhythms is key for hormone balance and health. Strategic fasting helps you harness the regeneration power during optimal windows while preventing hormone havoc from fasting too hard during sensitive times.

Issues surrounding the subject matter

1. How might the Fasting Cycle framework help women who have struggled with continuous fasting approaches that failed to account for hormonal fluctuations?

2. What insights does the alignment of fasting strategy with the Power, Manifestation, and Nurture phases provide for leveraging the benefits of fasting while avoiding disruption?

3. How could the concept of working cooperatively with innate hormonal rhythms rather than against them transform approaches to women's health and lifestyle choices?

Goals

1. One main goal is to time fasts right based on a woman's changing hormones. This helps support good health. Carefully matching how long and what kind of fasts to each phase of her cycle can make this work.

2. Another big goal is to trigger autophagy and ketosis through planned fasting. This gives cells a cleanse and supplies fuel to mitochondria. It keeps hormonal organs healthy.

3. One more major goal is to match lifestyle and diet to a woman's body. This promotes hormone balance. It means giving nourishment during sensitive times. It also means using her body's ability to regenerate during optimal times.

Action Steps

1. Time fasts based on hormone changes. For example, do longer 13-72 hour fasts during the Power Phase when sex hormones dip. This stimulates autophagy and ketosis for cellular cleansing and mitochondrial fueling. Also do longer fasts on days 16-19 when hormones decline after mid-cycle peaks.

2. Tailor diet to support each menstrual phase. For instance, eat hormone nourishing foods like cruciferous vegetables, salmon, and fermented foods during the Manifestation Phase to aid estrogen breakdown. Or eat starchy comfort foods like sweet potatoes and rice during the Nurture Phase to provide glucose for making progesterone.

3. Align lifestyle choices with your menstrual cycle. For example, reduce duties and avoid intense exercise during the Nurture Phase to lower stress and cortisol, which inhibits progesterone synthesis. Also avoid continuous extended fasting, as this can disrupt hormones if not aligned with your cycle.

Checklist

1. Time fasts properly - Do longer 13-72 hour fasts during Power Phase when sex hormones dip; Do shorter <15 hour fasts during Manifestation Phase when hormones peak.

2. Tailor diet to support phases - Eat hormone nourishing foods like cruciferous vegetables and salmon during Manifestation Phase; Consume starchy comfort foods during Nurture Phase to provide glucose for progesterone.

3. Align lifestyle with menstrual cycle - Reduce duties and avoid intense exercise during Nurture Phase to lower cortisol; Avoid continuous extended fasting that does not sync with cycle.

Part 3: The 30-Day Fasting Reset

Ch 8: The 30-Day Fasting Reset

The 30-day fasting reset plan detailed in the guide aims to help women integrate fasting into their lifestyle in a way that is tailored to their menstrual cycle. The reset has three main goals: metabolically flexing the body through different length fasts to promote adaptation, timing fasts according to the menstrual cycle phase, and doing the reset with community support.

The reset incorporates three fasting lengths ranging from 13 to 20 hours. These intermittent fasts provide enough stress to spur beneficial adaptation without being too difficult for beginners. During the 30 days, women will experience all phases of the fasting cycle including no fasting, intermittent fasting, autophagy fasting, and a gut reset fast. This variety of fasting lengths metabolically flexes the body, providing the hormetic stress needed to reap optimal benefits.

The reset is designed to be done from day 1 to the start of menstruation for women with a regular cycle. Those without a cycle can start anytime for a 30-day reset. The fasting schedule helps balance hormones in women without cycles, often restoring menstruation within 1-2 months. It also alleviates stubborn menopausal symptoms like hot flashes, sleep troubles, weight gain, belly fat, mood changes, and more.

Postmenopausal women often see great results doing this reset for 1-2 months, as it provides the hormonal balance needed after menopause's effect on hormones. Younger women with missed cycles likewise tend to regain menstrual cyclicity within the first month or two of regularly repeating this tailored fasting reset.

The author, Dr. Mindy Pelz cites research showing close relationships are pivotal for health and happiness. An 80-year Harvard study found tending to relationships to be a form of essential self-care, with lonely subjects dying earlier. Doing the reset with community support, whether through a book club, friend, or online group, sets women up for success via accountability and encouragement.

This reset works for women of all ages, but may be especially helpful for beginners looking to learn the fasting cycle, women without cycles wanting to restart menstruation, and those in menopause suffering from symptoms like hot flashes.

The reset can address many health conditions including: weight loss resistance, insulin resistance, diabetes, cardiovascular disease, autoimmunity, memory and mood problems, hormonal cancers, infertility, gut dysbiosis, menopause symptoms, brain fog, low energy, missed cycles, detox from birth control, thyroid disorders, hair loss, accelerated aging, and lack of motivation.

Women seeking to detox from birth control pills, antibiotics, or other medications may find this reset particularly useful for giving their body a fresh start. The focused gut reset fast helps repair gut lining damage, restoring the microbiome after antibiotic use.

As the body intermittently fasts, cells engage in autophagy, where dysfunctional components are recycled and new cellular parts built. This removes waste that accumulates over years, decreasing inflammation and risk of cancer and neurodegenerative disease. The fasting gives mitochondria a break from constant burning of glucose for energy production as well.

Intermittent fasting also sensitizes the body to insulin and leptin again, revving up metabolism. As women lose weight, insulin and testosterone levels lower, relieving PCOS and diabetes. Blood pressure and cholesterol profiles tend to improve, along with reversal of metabolic syndrome.

The cyclical nature of this reset creates ongoing mindfulness about how different fasts feel at various menstrual phases. Women become more attuned to their body's signals, learning how to tailor fasting to their unique needs. This diet variability inherent in the fasting cycle more closely matches ancestral eating patterns as well.

As always, women should consult their doctor before making major diet changes like this fasting reset. But this reset provides an evidence-based way for women to reap the many benefits of fasting in a sustainable, supportive manner tailored to their unique biology. By tuning into menstrual cues and fasting accordingly, women can biohack their way to better health.

The pre-reset is a 2-week period before starting the fasting reset intended to ease the body into this new eating pattern, especially for fasting beginners. There are 3 components: avoiding inflammatory foods, adding in healthy fats and proteins, and compressing the eating window.

First, processed foods with inflammatory oils, refined flours/sugars, and chemicals should be removed. This includes oils like canola, vegetable, and cottonseed which can disrupt hormones and spike hunger. Refined carbs and sweets cause blood sugar spikes and cravings as well. Chemicals like high fructose corn syrup and artificial sweeteners also dysregulate metabolism.

Second, satiating fats like olive oil, avocados, nuts, and proteins like eggs and grass-fed meats should be added. This stabilizes blood sugar and controls hunger by optimizing hormones like leptin and insulin. Cravings and energy crashes diminish.

Third, slowly compress the eating window by pushing breakfast back an hour every couple days until a 13 hour fast from dinner to breakfast is possible. For example, starting breakfast at 8 rather than 7, until it reaches 10. Black coffee, tea, water, and a touch of cream or MCT oil can be consumed to ease the transition.

This gradual adaptation helps the body switch from a constant glucose-burning to flexibly burning fat and ketones between meals. Hunger hormones adjust to facilitate fasting. Withdrawal from inflammatory foods prevents cravings. The pre-reset eases the body into fat burning mode so the 30-day reset can be completed with less difficulty.

Rather than a drastic, stressful change, this pre-reset incrementally transitions the body's metabolic patterns while removing inflammatory inputs. Like a warm up before exercise, it poises the body for success in adopting intermittent fasting long-term by slowly building tolerance in a supported manner.

During the reset, temptations should be removed from home and work to prevent derailment. Naysayers who may threaten progress should be avoided in favor of positive, supportive people.

The reset has 3 phases: <u>2 "power" ketobiotic phases with varied length fasts, and one "nurture" phase with no fasting.</u> The first power phase fasts 13 hours for 4 days, 15 hours on day 5, then 17 hour autophagy fasts on days 6-10. The manifestation phase returns to 13 hour fasts with hormone-supporting foods for days 11-15 before the second power phase.

<u>Power phase 2</u> intermittently fasts 15 hours for 4 days. The nurture phase from days 20-30 involves no fasting and hormone-balancing foods. Throughout, inflammatory oils,

refined carbs/sugars, chemicals and alcohol are avoided. The varied fasting lengths provide hormetic stress to spur beneficial adaptation.

The cyclical nature of the program creates metabolic flexibility. Fasting is timed strategically in each phase to leverage hormones for optimal health. Supportive foods stabilize blood sugar. Different fasts become easier with practice as the body improves regulation of glucose and hunger cues.

Planning your reset start time wisely with the menstrual and social calendars can set up success. Once adapted, occasional events like weddings or vacations can be navigated with flexibility. Creating accountability and community provides additional support.

With preparation and strategic fasting tailored to the menstrual cycle, the reset creates metabolic shifts that maximize hormone health. As women tune into their body's needs, fasting gets easier. With consistent practice, intermittent fasting can become a sustainable lifestyle for improved wellbeing.

Timing is key - starting the reset at the right point in the menstrual cycle and when social obligations are lower sets women up for adherence. Patience through a transition period pays off long-term. Support from health-minded friends prevents derailment from naysayers. While challenging at first, preparation combined with an incremental approach creates lifelong healthy intermittent fasting habits.

The advanced fasting reset is for experienced fasters seeking greater challenge through longer fasts like 24 hours. It still follows a cyclical format timed to menstrual phases. There are 2 ketobiotic power phases with varied length fasts and one nurture phase with no fasting.

The longer fasts provide a more robust hormetic stress to encourage greater adaptation. The week before menstruation can optionally include shorter 13 hour fasts to avoid cortisol spikes. Food choices remain anti-inflammatory during the power phases and hormone supporting during the nurture phase.

Self-tracking biometrics like blood glucose and ketones helps optimize the experience. A glucose monitor can be used to check morning blood sugar and ketones after overnight fasting, right before eating to see if ketones increased indicating fat burning, and 2 hours after a meal to assess insulin sensitivity based on how quickly blood sugar returns to baseline.

Seeing blood sugar drop and ketones rise from morning to pre-meal illustrates the body transitioning from burning glucose to burning fat for energy during the fasting period. Ketones above 0.5 mmol/L indicate establishment of ketosis. If blood sugar is close to baseline 2 hours after eating, insulin sensitivity improves.

While challenging at first, metabolic flexibility grows with consistency. The body becomes better at burning fat between meals, regulating hunger signals, and maintaining balanced blood sugar when following a structured intermittent fasting routine.

Advanced fast practitioners may appreciate the accelerated adaptation generated by longer fasts. However, patience and self-compassion remain important, as progress occurs incrementally. Support from the community and tracking biometrics prevents discouragement when obstacles arise. The first Advanced Power phase fasts 15 hours for 5 days, 24 hours on day 6, then 17-hour autophagy fasts on days 7-10. The manifestation phase returns to 15 hour fasts with hormone-supporting foods on days 11-15 before the second power phase.

Advanced Power phase 2 does a 24-hour gut reset fast on day 16, then 17 hour fasts for days 17-19. The nurture phase from days 20-30 involves 13 hour intermittent fasting and hormone-balancing foods

The advanced reset's fasting lengths are engineered to spark deep metabolic shifts for experienced fasters. Strategic meal timing and ketogenic food choices facilitate the process. Though demanding, the reset's measured progression allows the body to rise to the challenge. Listen to your body's signals, celebrate small victories, and you'll be amazed at the transformation.

The 24 hour fasts in particular provide an intense hormetic stress. Research shows fasting this long gives the digestive system a break, allows old immune cells to be cleared out and new ones generated, and compels the body to derive energy from fat stores resulting in rapid weight loss. Fasting stimulates human growth hormone production as well for anti-aging benefits.

However, longer fasts deplete glycogen stores and may be difficult for beginners. So, the advanced reset strategically programs the 24 hour fasts after several weeks of metabolic conditioning from shorter fasts. This primes the body to burn fat and ketones efficiently when glucose becomes scarce from prolonged fasting.

Supporting the longer fasts are ketogenic food choices that keep insulin levels low while providing energy from fat and protein. Stable blood sugar and satiety prevent intense hunger during the fasting periods. Once adapted, fasting becomes almost effortless.

The cyclical nature of the program allows the body to consolidate the gains made during the power phases when returning to shorter fasts or no fasting during the nurture phase. This metabolic flexibility matches our ancestral eating patterns more closely than constant calorie restriction.

The advanced reset's intelligent design elicits transformative change for experienced fasters. The phased introduction of longer fasts coupled with hormone-supporting foods optimizes the health benefits of fasting while ensuring sustainability. Consistency and community get you through the challenging moments on your fasting journey.

Lessons

1. Fasting in a strategic, cyclical manner provides hormetic stress that spurs beneficial adaptation. The varied lengths of fasts in the different phases metabolically flex the body and elicit transformative change.

2. Timing fasting and feeding windows appropriately to the menstrual cycle leverages hormonal fluctuations for optimal health. Strategic meal timing facilitates metabolic shifts.

3. Preparation and community support are key to successfully adopting fasting long-term. A transition period eases the body into metabolic flexibility. Patience and cheerleaders prevent discouragement.

Issues surrounding the subject matter

1. How can women determine the optimal intermittent fasting routine that provides hormetic stress while remaining sustainable long-term? What signals and biomarkers could help guide appropriate fasting lengths?

2. What strategies can women employ to time their fasting and feeding windows strategically according to their menstrual cycle phase? How can they leverage hormonal fluctuations most effectively?

3. What kinds of preparation and support systems can enable women to successfully adopt intermittent fasting as an ongoing lifestyle? What potential obstacles may arise and how can they be addressed proactively?

Goals

1. The reset aims to metabolically flex the body through different lengths of intermittent fasting. It's designed to provide just enough hormetic stress to spur adaptation without overdoing it. Like strength training builds muscle through progressive overload, strategic fasting stresses the body toward positive change.

2. The reset times fasting periods and feeding windows according to the menstrual cycle. The idea is to work with, not against, a woman's hormonal fluctuations for optimal health. It leverages biology rather than fights it.

3. The reset encourages doing this fasting journey together with community support. Sisterhood and accountability partners make adopting lasting lifestyle changes much more doable. We all need cheerleaders in our corner.

Action Steps

1. Gradually transition into fasting through a pre-reset period of avoiding inflammatory foods, adding healthy fats/proteins, and compressing the eating window (e.g. move breakfast back incrementally each day).

2. Time fasting periods are strategically based on the menstrual cycle phase for hormonal leverage (e.g. shorter fasts pre-menstruation, longer fasts after).

3. Join an online community or enlist friends to provide fasting support and accountability (e.g. through a virtual group, book club, or buddies).

Checklist

1. Pick a fasting plan that pushes you out of your comfort zone—but not too far! The sweet spot is intermittent fasting that's challenging yet sustainable. Build up fasting stamina slowly over time for a smooth transition.

2. Sync fasting periods with your menstrual cycle. Hormones ebb and flow, so fasting strategies should too. Work with your body's natural rhythms rather than against them for the best results.

3. Get your fasting squad ready! Having buddies for accountability and encouragement makes it so much easier to stick to those fasting windows long-term. A little support goes a long way when you hit inevitable obstacles.

Ch 9: How to Break a Fast

Summary

In this chapter, Dr. Mindy Pelz discusses strategies for breaking a fast in order to optimize health benefits. It is noted that research on how to properly break a fast has been limited, so she did her own research by testing different approaches on thousands of people. She found there are four main strategies for breaking a fast, depending on your goals:

1. Reset the microbiome - Break fast with probiotics, prebiotics and polyphenols to feed good gut bacteria. Examples are yogurt, sauerkraut, seeds. This helps if you've taken antibiotics or want better immunity.

2. Build muscle - Break fast with protein sources like eggs, jerky or shakes. The protein triggers muscle growth after fasting. Good for women over 40 who want to maintain muscle.

3. Keep burning fat - Break fast with fats like avocado, nuts, oils. This keeps the body in fat burning mode longer. Helpful for extending fasts.

4. Follow tastebuds - Break fast with whatever sounds good. Provides satisfaction but may not optimize health goals. Daily 14-16 hour fasts can still provide benefits.

Dr. Pelz then explains that what breaks a fast depends on microbiome diversity and insulin sensitivity. A blood sugar test is suggested to see if a food pulls you out of fasting.

She also points out that beverages that typically don't affect fasting are black coffee, tea, mineral water. Beverages that often break a fast are coffee creamers, sweeteners, soda, diet soda, alcohol.

A "fasted snack" of small amount of fat may prolong fasts for beginners. Suggestions are nut butter, cream, oils. Use snacks as crutch until adapted to fasting.

For fasts over 48 hours, a gradual refeeding process is recommended. Steps are: broth, probiotic meal, steamed veggies, then animal protein or high protein plant foods. This slowly restarts digestion.

Dr. Pelz strongly emphasizes that properly breaking a fast is just as important as fasting itself. A lot of people think fasting is simple - you just stop eating for a while. But there's more nuance to it if you want to get the full health benefits.

The takeaway is to be thoughtful and strategic when breaking a fast if you want to amplify the health perks. Don't get frustrated by the details of how food impacts your blood sugar. There are many personalized factors at play. But being intentional with refeeding is key for results.

Lessons

1. How you break your fast matters just as much as the fasting itself. Rushing into eating whatever after fasting can totally ruin those health gains you worked for. You got to be strategic with that first meal to really get the benefits.

2. There's no one "right way" to break a fast that works for everyone. We all have different health goals and sensitivities. *I need to figure out what works best for my own body* - a blood sugar test can help with that.

3. Don't sweat the small stuff when it comes to how food impacts your blood sugar. Lots of little things can affect it so don't get frustrated. Just focus on being intentional with that first meal after fasting and finding what works for you. The results will come.

Issues Surrounding the Subject Matter

1. What are your health goals when it comes to fasting? Are you aiming to reset your microbiome, build muscle, burn fat or something else? Knowing your aims can help determine the best strategy for breaking your fast.

2. Have you experimented with different approaches to breaking your fast to see what works best for your body? A blood sugar test can provide insight on how

different foods impact you. What foods have you found break your fast or prolong it?

3. How intentional are you about that first meal after fasting? Do you carefully consider portions, food choices and timing or break your fast with whatever sounds good? How could you be more strategic with refeeding to amplify your fasting benefits?

Goals

1. <u>Getting my gut back on track</u> - Fasting can really help reset your microbiome, especially if you've been on antibiotics or something. Eating fermented foods and stuff with probiotics when you break the fast keeps that good bacteria growing.

2. <u>Dropping a few pounds</u> - A lot of people fast to burn some fat and lose weight. Sticking to healthy fats and proteins when you break the fast keeps you in fat burning mode longer.

3. <u>Cutting down inflammation</u> - Fasting can reduce inflammation, so following it up with a ton of antioxidant-rich fruits and veggies doubles down on the anti-inflammatory effects.

Action Steps

1. Know your goals - If you're fasting for gut health, break with some sauerkraut or yogurt for the probiotics.

2. Test your response - Check your blood sugar after having coffee with half and half to see if it kicks you out of fasting.

3. Go slow after longer fasts - After fasting for a few days, first do bone broth, then some avocado, then steamed veggies before a full meal.

Checklist

1. Get clear on why you were fasting in the first place - Were you trying to improve gut health, burn fat, build muscle? Knowing your goal helps pick the right foods to break the fast.

2. Test your blood sugar with different foods - See what spikes your levels, indicating it breaks your fasted state. This lets you know what to avoid eating first.

3. Go slow after longer fasts - Don't shock your system if you've fasted for over 2 days. Slowly reintroduce broth, fermented foods, veggies and then protein.

Ch 10: Hacks That Make Fasting Effortless

Summary

In this segment, Mindy Pelz starts by acknowledging that she is impatient and always looking for the fastest way to get results when fasting. She cautions that while hacks can accelerate healing, the goal isn't always speed. She outlines three principles:

First, healing takes time, especially for chronic conditions. Fasters should be patient and keep at their fasting lifestyle to give their body opportunities to heal.

Second, fasting is a new skill that takes practice. Don't get discouraged by imperfect days. Look at each fast as progress, since any period of fasting puts the body in a healing state.

Third, keep learning about how the body works. This knowledge makes integrating fasting easier. The author says the more you know about fasting, the easier it is to create a lifestyle that works for you.

She then shares common hacks her community uses to excel at fasting:

For hunger, first determine if you're actually hungry or just bored. Do a mood-boosting activity first. If still hungry, mineral supplements like LMNT and Redmond packets can help by correcting mineral imbalances that cause hunger. Sipping these in water during a fast helps. If still hungry, a small "fat bomb" like cream and MCT oil in coffee can bridge the gap to a longer fast. Feed gut microbes prebiotics in a fasted state, as hunger is sometimes their signal for food.

For coffee and tea, choose organic, mold-free coffee, as chemical-laden coffee can spike blood sugar. "Clean" coffee won't hinder insulin sensitivity.

For detox symptoms like keto flu, vary fasts to reduce toxin buildup. Open detox pathways through skin brushing, sweating, lymph massage, rebounding ("rebounding" here refers to using a mini-trampoline as a form of exercise to aid detoxification and improve lymph and circulatory function.), and Epsom salt baths. Use zeolite and charcoal supplements to hold on to toxins released when detoxing.

To measure blood sugar and ketones, avoid inaccurate urine and breath methods. Recommended are blood sugar/ketone meters (with finger prick blood) and continuous glucose monitors to see food impacts. Watch for dropping blood sugar and rising ketones as the body switches to fat burning. Signs of ketosis are lack of hunger, mental clarity, steady energy and ketone readings of 0.5 mmol/L or higher on a meter.

At the start of a fasting plan, your blood sugar could stay elevated for a while, even with proper fasting techniques. This happens when first training the body to be a fat burner. The first goal is getting into ketosis, but what if you do everything right and still don't reach ketosis? There are six hacks to try.

Extend fasting duration - A 36-hour fast can flip the metabolic switch to fat burning. More fasting stress can push the body into ketosis.

Vary fasting routine - Varying fasts instead of sticking to the same routine, which can stall progress. Our bodies adapt to routine, so changing up fasting durations and types keeps cells metabolically flexible.

Avoid all processed foods - Bad oils, refined sugars and flours, and chemicals make insulin resistance worse, blocking ketosis despite fasting. Remember the standard American diet causes inflammation and insulin resistance. Oils, sugar, and chemicals are the big health insults.

Support liver function - Loving your liver, which senses dropping blood sugar and switches to ketosis. Congestion prevents this, so minimize alcohol and toxins. Essential oils, castor oil packs, coffee enemas, bitter greens, and dandelion tea can improve liver function.

Manage adrenal fatigue - Adrenals work with the brain, so communication issues cause dysfunction. Dizziness when standing or salt cravings indicate adrenal fatigue. Testing for adrenal issues and supplements can help.

Remove heavy metal toxins - Toxins damage the liver and increase insulin resistance. Detox may be needed if other strategies fail.

When fasting, open detox pathways accelerate weight loss. Gaining weight while fasting indicates congestion in the liver, gut, kidneys, lymph and skin. Have daily bowel movements, sweat, hydrate, dry brush, use castor oil packs, and get lymphatic massage. This prevents storing toxins in fat.

For women, spotting or missed cycles while fasting can mean low progesterone. This is common and not concerning. In fact, fasting repairs damage, stimulating healing. Lengthening or irregular cycles are also common in perimenopause. Trying two rounds of the 30-day fasting reset can help stabilize cycles.

Hair loss while fasting is common but avoidable. Take mineral supplements, vary fasting lengths, and avoid fasts over 17 hours. If hair loss persists, test for heavy metals like lead, mercury, and thallium, which prevent mineral absorption. Thallium from fish can worsen hair loss. Chemicals from breast implants also contribute. Removing implants improves symptoms.

Fatigue while fasting is normal as you repair mitochondria. Allow extra rest and sleep. If fatigue persists, use red light therapy to power mitochondria. Hyperbaric oxygen also improves cellular oxygenation and mitochondria function. Detoxing may help if fasting doesn't provide energy.

Medications like thyroid medicine may require adjustments when fasting. Take them during eating windows or with coffee to avoid sensitivity from fasting. Involve your doctor in medication changes with fasting.

Supplement timing is flexible with shorter fasts. Take with food if nauseated when fasting. Avoid supplements during three-day fasts, allowing the body to control reactions.

Cravings arise from mineral imbalance and microbiome changes. Supplement minerals and persist through carb and sugar cravings as bad gut bacteria die off.

When falling off fasting, release judgment and resume the next day. Fasting gets easier with practice, so see lapses during training as progress.

Some need less sleep while fasting as repair occurs during both sleep and fasting. Embrace early waking for spiritual practices. Aches during longer fasts are likely stem cell repairs. Increase magnesium and try CBD oil to ease discomfort.

Exercise while fasted during shorter fasts boosts fat burning. Don't exercise during three-day fasts, allowing complete repair mode.

The 30-day reset maximizes sex hormone production to support the body after hysterectomies.

Fasting helps thyroid function by repairing brain neurons, healing the gut for conversion of T4 to T3, and lowering inflammation for hormone cell uptake. Studies show only temporary T3 reductions that increase after fasting.

For adrenal fatigue, slowly increase fasting times over weeks and stabilize blood sugar. Seek practitioner support if adrenals are very compromised.

Do not fast while pregnant or nursing as toxins release into the baby. Short 13 hour fasts while nursing may be safe with medical guidance.

Diabetics can thrive with fasting but severely ill patients should be supervised and monitor blood sugar carefully. Share research on fasting benefits with unfamiliar doctors.

Those with past eating disorders should involve their doctor to fast safely. Watch for restricting calories, skipping meals randomly, or self-judgment. Stop fasting if it doesn't feel positive.

Lessons

1. Rome wasn't built in a day. Fasting is a lifestyle change that takes time to adapt to. You'll likely hit some bumps in the road where your fasts don't go as planned. But don't sweat it! Every fast is bringing you one step closer to your goals. Progress isn't always linear. As long as you keep learning and stick with it, you'll get there.

2. Listen to your body's signals and tweak your approach accordingly. If you're struggling with hunger, headaches, or low energy during your fasts, take that feedback and troubleshoot. Experiment with things like electrolytes, herbal teas, or shorter fasts until you find what works best for you. There are so many little tricks you can try to make fasting more sustainable.

3. Chat with your doctor, especially if you have health issues that could be impacted by fasting. They may have insight into how to fast safely with your condition, what signs to watch out for, or whether any medication adjustments are needed. It never hurts to involve your healthcare provider when making big lifestyle changes. Their guidance can prevent any unnecessary hiccups.

Issues Surrounding the Subject Matter

1. Fasting takes time to see results - it's not a quick fix! For those who have tried fasting, how long did it take you to really notice changes? I'm curious about realistic timelines. A few days? A few weeks? A few months?

2. The summary talked about using tricks like electrolyte supplements to make fasting easier. I wonder what kind of hurdles others have run into while fasting. Headaches? Hunger pangs? Low energy? What do you think may work for you to get over those humps?

3. Involving a doctor for pre-existing conditions was advised in the summary. If you have a health condition, did you consult your doctor before starting a fasting regimen? Did their guidance help make fasting more effective or safe for your situation?

Goals

1. Patience pays off. Implementing fasting as an ongoing lifestyle takes time for your body to get used to. You may hit some bumps in the road or plateaus where your progress stalls. Stick with it! Consistency and commitment will pay dividends in the long run.

2. Listen to your body. Pay attention to any hunger pangs, headaches, or low energy you experience while fasting. Your body will give you signals. Use them to customize your approach - maybe you need more fluids, shorter fasts, electrolytes, etc. Find what works best for YOU.

3. Consult your doc. If you have any ongoing health conditions, touch base with your doctor before diving into fasting. They can provide guidance specific to your situation, any precautions to take, and what signs to look out for. Their input will help you fast safely and effectively.

Action Steps

1. Get set up for fasting victory - Keep go-to items like mineral supplements and soothing teas available. They can help ease issues like hunger and stress during fasts.

2. Adapt your method over time - If certain fasting durations don't work for you, change them up. For example, if 16-hour fasts zap your energy, try starting with 14 hours and building back up slowly. Or add bone broth during fasts if hunger is a major hurdle.

3. Optimize related lifestyle factors - Make sleep a bigger priority to support longer fasts, since repair happens while sleeping. And use extra morning time from waking early for spiritual practices like meditation or prayer.

Checklist

1. Before you start:
    a. Talk to your doc if you have health stuff going on, just to play it safe. Get their green light.
    b. Stock up on supplements and teas to make fasting comfortable. Gotta think ahead!
    c. Remember this is a marathon, not a sprint! It takes time to see results. Keep expectations realistic.

2. During your fasts:
    a. Listen to signals from your body like hunger or headaches. Tweak your plan until it feels right.
    b. Stay on top of detoxing - dry brush, massage, Epsom salts. Help your body out!
    c. Don't beat yourself up for slip ups! Just restart the next day. Progress isn't always linear.

3. Long-term habits:
    a. Commit for the long haul! Remind yourself this is an ongoing lifestyle.
    b. Keep learning about your body's unique responses. Dial in what works for YOU.
    c. Surround yourself with a solid support system. Community can keep you motivated.

Conclusion

The time for change is now. After reviewing the science, historical context, and practical guidance in this fasting workbook, the path ahead is clear. Intermittent fasting, when practiced strategically, can be profoundly healing and liberating. The body is primed to thrive with the very lifestyle practiced by our ancestors - cycles of feast and famine in alignment with natural rhythms.

Yet we have lost touch with this ancestral wisdom that our physiology intrinsically understands. The results are poor health, lack of energy, and chronic disease. But the body's remarkable capacity to self-repair remains latent within, awaiting the proper conditions to express its potential. Intermittent fasting provides this healing impetus to renew health from a cellular level.

The way forward requires courage, openness, patience, and community. Progress will not always be linear. At times the journey may prove challenging. But armed with knowledge, women can rewrite limiting narratives about their health. Supporting each other, we can overcome inertia and fear. If thousands of others can transform their wellbeing through educated fasting, so too can you!

Imagine the vitality that will come as your cells are freed of dysfunction accumulated over decades. Envision the focus and productivity that arises when inflammation resides and hormones recalibrate. Believe in your body's inherent drive to return to balance when supported. Walk boldly toward the best version of yourself.

Now is the time to embody your desires. Everything has fallen into place for you to start this fasting journey. Your equally motivated friends from the like-minded community are cheering you on, eager to see you succeed. You have the power within to achieve this. Listen to your inner wisdom - <u>it's time to start your fasting journey.</u>